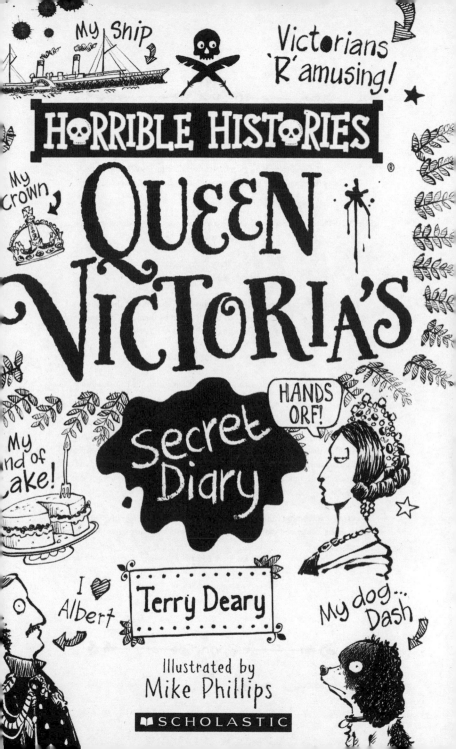

My SHIP

Victorians 'R' amusing!

HORRIBLE HIST⚟RIES ®

My CROWN

QUEEN VICT⚟RIA'S

Secret Diary

HANDS ORF!

My nd of ake!

I ♥ Albert

Terry Deary

My dog... Dash

Illustrated by
Mike Phillips

SCHOLASTIC

Published in the UK by Scholastic, 2021
Euston House, 24 Eversholt Street, London, NW1 1DB
Scholastic Ireland, 89E Lagan Road, Dublin Industrial Estate, Glasnevin,
Dublin, D11 HP5F

Text © Terry Deary, 2021
Illustrations © Mike Phillips, 2021

The right of Terry Deary and Mike Phillips to be identified as the author and
illustrators of this work respectively has been asserted by them in accordance with the
Copyright, Designs and Patents Act, 1988.

ISBN 978 07023 0666 2

A CIP catalogue record for this book is available from the British Library.

Printed and bound in the UK by CPI Group (UK) Ltd, Croydon, CR0 4YY
Paper made from wood grown in sustainable forests and other controlled sources.

1 3 5 7 9 10 8 6 4 2

www.scholastic.co.uk

CONTENTS

26 June 1830	11
18 May 1836	16
20 June 1837	20
28 June 1838	21
1 August 1838	26
20 April 1839	33
15 August 1839	38
10 February 1840	41
10 August 1842	47
30 March 1843	55
21 November 1845	57
10 April 1848	60
12 August 1849	63
11 September 1849	68
27 September 1849	69
1 May 1851	74
11 November 1853	80
20 September 1854	83
4 November 1854	87
8 September 1857	89
25 September 1857	92
23 December 1861	95
10 January 1863	100
20 June 1867	104
26 May 1868	107
30 March 1869	112
9 June 1870	114
1 May 1873	117
23 January 1875	122
1 May 1876	124
28 December 1879	126
19 April 1881	129
2 March 1882	134
29 March 1883	142
16 November 1888	147
1 July 1890	151
10 June 1896	152
20 November 1896	155
22 June 1897	157
24 May 1899	158
31 December 1900	161
22 January 1901	164
Epilogue	166

That's ME!
QUEEN VICTORIA →

I'm soooooooo
PRETTY!

Daddy

Mummy

Duke of Kent
1767 – 1820

Duchess of Kent
1786 – 1861

Me,
looking pretty
marvellous!

Queen Victoria
1819 – ?

Victoria
1840 – 1901

Married:
Emperor
Frederick III

Children:

Wilhelm II.
Charotte.
Prince Henry.
Prince Sigismund.
Princess Viktoria.
Prince Waldemar.
Queen Sophia.
Margaret.

Edward VII
1841 – 1910

Married:
Alexandra
of Denmark

Children:

Prince Albert.
George V.
Princess Louis.
Princess Victoria.
Queen Maud.
Prince Alexander.

Alice
1843 – 1878

Married:
Grand Duke
Louis IV

Children:

Victoria.
Duchess Elizabeth.
Princess Irene.
Duke Ernest.
Prince Friedrich.
Empress Alix.
Princess Marie.

Alfred
1844 – 1900

Married:
Grand Duchess
Maria

Children:

Prince Alfred.
Queen Marie.
Duchess Victoria.
Princess Alexandra.
Princess Beatrice.

My family tree

Prince Albert
1819 – 1861

Hubby

Our Kids

Helena
1846–1923

Married:
Prince
Christian

Children:

Prince Christian.
Princess Helena.
Princess Marie.

Louise
1848–1939

Married:
Duke
John Campbell

Children:

None!

Arthur
1850–1942

Married:
Princess
Louise

Children:

Princess
Margaret.

Prince
Arthur.

Princess
Patricia.

Leopold
1853–1884

Married:
Princess
Helena

Children:

Princess
Alice.

Charles.

Beatrice
1857–1944

Married:
Prince
Henry

Children:

Alexander.
Queen
Victoria Eugenie.
Lord Leopold.
Prince Maurice.

Victorians
R
Amusing!

26 June 1830

This morning Mother called me to her room with the sad, sad news.

I have sad news. Your Uncle George has died, and your Uncle William will become King.

How sad!

I wept. Then I went to our bedroom and I danced. You see what this means? When Uncle William dies, I shall become queen. Oh, joy.

I have to be 18 before I can rule. Otherwise Mother shall rule for me. I would hate that. But jolly old Uncle William has promised to stay alive till after my 18th birthday.

Of course, Uncle King George IV died because he was too fat to live. Before he was king, he was Prince of Wales. A shocking (but funny) poem called him ...

By his bulk and by his size,
By his oily qualities,
This (unless my eyesight fails)
This should be the Prince of Whales.

How I giggled at that poem. But I only
giggled when I was alone with my Spaniel,
Dash. I visited my uncle a few days ago and
his maidservant passed me a list of what he
needed for breakfast.

Breakfast

3: Pigeons

3: Beef steaks

A bottle of wine

A glass of Champagne

2: Glasses of port

A glass of brandy

No wonder the street children sing about him,
'Georgie Porgy pudding and pie'.

At least he rebuilt Buckingham Palace and
Windsor Castle, and I shall use them when
I become queen.

The new king, his brother William IV, is much
more fun. He never expected to be king, so
he thinks it is all a great joke. He was in the
navy from the age of 13. He did his share of
the cooking on the ship and he once got

arrested with his shipmates after a drunken fight in Gibraltar. (That is a family secret. No one printed it in the newspapers.)

They call him 'Sailor Bill'.

Uncle William IV

I shall NOT be cooking OR fighting when I am queen. I shall be wise and beautiful. See how beautiful I am ...

Beautiful Me!

Uncle William has a great time riding out in his carriage so the people can see him. I shall do that. If he sees someone respectable walking along, he stops and offers them a lift. I shall NOT be doing that. I am a handsome lady, not a hansom cab. (A little joke. I am fond of jokes.)

The funeral of Uncle King George will be at Windsor. I shall dress in black and look sad. When the coffin-carriers stagger under the weight of the whale I shall try not to laugh. Honestly, secret diary, I shall really try – but it will be hard.

18 May 1836

Secret Diary, I have often told you how much my mother bullies me and controls me. She has an awful man to advise her – Sir John Conroy. Between them they treat me like a dog. No, they do not. I treat my Dash much better than they treat me.

Mother has the idea that Uncle King William will die before I am 18. Then she will rule all of Britain until I am old enough. Please live another year, Uncle King William.

My poor father died when I was just 8 months old, so I do not have anyone to save me from her. She makes strict rules for me. I must:

- Go to lessons with special tutors
- learn French, German, Italian, and Latin (ugh)
- spend hardly any time with other children

- 🕷 always be watched by some adult and never ever be left alone

- 🕷 share a bedroom with mother

- 🕷 be paraded around country houses and shown off like a prize pig

- 🕷 always walk downstairs without someone holding my hand

- 🕷 never meet my father's family

I do wish I had known my father. Some people were unkind about him. Of course, his pictures show he was bald.

Duke of Kent
Daddy

17

A playwriter called Richard Sheridan said ...

> *He is bald because he hasn't enough brain to feed the hair on the outside. Grass does not grow upon deserts.*

Luckily, Mr Sheridan died before I was born, or I would have him thrown into jail for his insult. Jail for fifty years. Nasty man.

But, as I was saying, my mother is a monster. But today I forgive her. I forgive her for being a bully who sits on me like a hen sits on an egg. Because today she brought two guests to our house. They are my cousins, Albert of Saxe-Coburg, and Ernest.

In my diary (my royal diary, not this secret one) I wrote:

Albert is extremely handsome; his hair is about the same colour as mine; his eyes

18

are large and blue, and he has a beautiful nose and a very sweet mouth with fine teeth; but the charm of his face is his expression, which is most delightful.

That is what I wrote. But I can tell you, my Secret Diary, I love him even more than that. Albert is the most beautiful thing I have ever seen. One day I shall marry him. He cannot ASK me to marry – no man can ask a queen to marry her. So, I shall have to ask HIM.

Albert

Uncle King William wants me to marry Prince Alexander of the Netherlands, but he is as plain as a pudding next to my handsome Albert.

THANK YOU, MY DEAREST MOTHER. THANK YOU.

20 June 1837

Poor old, dear old Uncle King William has died. Mother hated Uncle King William and will not let me go to his funeral. But who cares? He lived long enough for me to have my 18th birthday. I can rule without meddling mother or cruel Conroy.

I. Am. Queen.

I must act sadly and not dance around to show my joy.

But I. Am. Queen.

Yahoo!

28 June 1838

Thank goodness that is over. I mean my coronation of course.

Four hundred THOUSAND people lined the streets just to see their new queen go to Westminster Abbey to be crowned. How they love me. How they cheered and sang and waved flags. Those lucky people KNOW how they are blessed to have a queen like me.

The wonderful new railways brought people to London from far and wide. I do love trains. The showmen had a huge fair in Hyde park with trips in hot-air balloons. But really, the people came to catch a view of their new and amazing queen in her gold state coach. Sadly, my golden coach was held up for nearly an hour because it tangled with the traffic carrying goods to the fair. It isn't fair. (Oh, my jokes are the best).

But that coronation. Oh dear. It went on for
FIVE hours. I changed dresses twice. At least
I could go out from time to time into the little
St. Edward's Chapel where there were tables
of sandwiches to eat and wine to drink.

My dress was wonderful. The train was so
long it took eight ladies to carry it. As
I said, I do love trains. (And I do love making
jokes. That was another one.)

But we had no practice so no one really
knew what they were doing and of course
things went wrong.

There were around 250 singers and players,
but the music was awful. Thomas Atwood was
working on a new anthem for today. He died 3
months ago so it was never finished. Old fool.

It was awful when Lord Rolle climbed the steps
to my throne and tried to bow. He is 82 years
old and very frail. As he bowed, he fell over
backwards down the steps. He Rolle-d. (I was

awake at 4 o'clock this morning, and am weary, but I can still make a joke.) I stepped forward to help him and the Abbey shook with cheers for my kindness. The thing is, two of my lords were supposed to help old Rolle up the stairs, but they let go too soon. Old fools.

The archbishop put the royal ring on the wrong finger, and it was stuck. Then he told me it was all over when it was not. He was looking at the book  of all the things we had to do. He turned over two pages at once and skipped an important part. I began to walk out – just as he told me to – and I had to turn around and walk back. Another old fool.

At last the beautiful crown was placed on my head and I feel truly like a queen. Now I must go on to be the greatest queen in the world. And that is not a joke, dear diary.

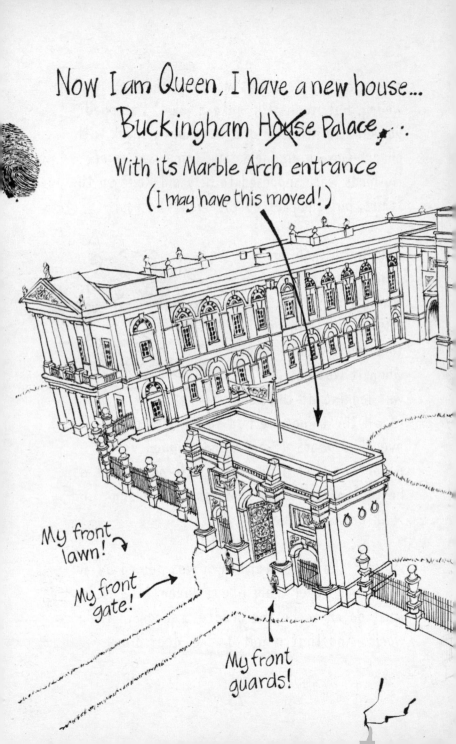

1 August 1838

Today a new law was passed. It finally banned British people from owning slaves anywhere in the world. 768,000 slaves are free today. But many native lords in our Empire countries keep slaves and we Brits cannot do anything about it.

I have to say that not everyone agreed with this new law. A Scottish writer called James Boswell said ...

Slaves are owned by people. So, taking the slaves away from their owner is robbery. Banning slavery is cruel to the slaves, especially the Africans. Being a slave to the British Empire has given many of them a much happier life.

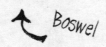

← Boswel

Other people, men like William Wilberforce said slavery was cruel. He died before he saw this law to ban slavery. But he once told me why it was so horrible.

Slave owners are free to punish slaves in terrible ways. The slave may be nailed to a post by the ear or even have that ear cut off. Others pull out the teeth or cut off the slave's hands. Many are fastened in tight steel neck-collars. The worst slave-owners gouge out the eyes.

Wilberforce →

A freed slave wrote a book and a lot of people took notice. He was Olaudah Equiano.

Olaudah Equiano

I read his book. I remember he said ...

The adults of our village used to go off to work in the fields. The children then gathered together to play. But whenever we played, we always sent someone up a tree to watch out for slave dealers. This was the time when slave dealers rushed into the village, snatched as many children as they could, and carried them off to the coast. There they were sold as slaves.

Slaves were worth a lot of money, but the traders did not take very good care of them on the ships that carried them across the world. Many died, packed into dark, stinking rooms below the decks of the ships. The sailors said they did wash the slaves down every day – probably a bucket of sea water thrown over them.

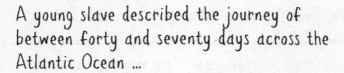

A young slave described the journey of between forty and seventy days across the Atlantic Ocean ...

The stench and the heat was dreadful. The crowding meant you hardly had room to turn over. The chains rubbed some Africans raw. The filth was made worse by the lavatory bucket and many small children fell into it. One day two of my countrymen were allowed on deck. They were chained together and decided they would rather have death than such a life of misery. They jumped into the sea. On long journeys food and fresh water supplies got low. The captain would throw weak slaves - alive - into the ocean so the fit could survive. Slaves who died were usually thrown over the side to feed the fishes. Others arrived in America very sick.

My British people have put an end to that. But the Americans go on keeping slaves to pick their cotton and their sugar cane.

It is sad that we need their cotton and sugar. We still enjoy the work of slaves even though we don't have any ourselves.

I have even read about people in Britain who think we treat our workers like slaves in the weaving mills of the north.

I work at the silk mill. I am an overlooker and I have to manage the children at the mill. Their strength gets weaker towards the evening and they get tired. I have been forced to make them work when I knew they could not bear it. I have been disgusted with myself. I felt myself ashamed and working like a slave-driver.

William Rastrick, Supervisor, 1832.

Maybe one day we can set the children free. But for now, they are needed to make the cotton and silk cloth that I love. And they are very cheap, so they must struggle on a little longer.

But my people will never be slaves. Our old British song is coming true:

When Britain first, at Heaven's command
Arose from out the azure main;
This was the charter of the land,
And guardian angels sang this strain:
'Rule, Britannia! rule the waves:
'Britons never will be slaves.'

Two British steam-ships crossed the Atlantic Ocean back in April. The inventor Mr Isambard Brunel built the 'Great Western'. In future he will build iron ships instead of wooden ones.

No more worrying about winds and storms. We can rule the waves and the world with ease. We can put guns and soldiers on our ships and conquer distant countries. There will be no end to the British Empire.

MY EMPIRE.

OOOPS!

20 April 1839

Now that I am queen, I do not have to do boring lessons in Latin and history and all that. I can read books for my own pleasure. And I have come across a young man who writes the most marvellous and tender books. His name is Charles Dickens. Even if he never writes another book, his 'Oliver Twist - The Parish Boy's Progress' will be remembered forever.

I loved the scene in the workhouse where the hero - Oliver Twist - goes to the workhouse keeper and asks for another helping of food.

Child as he was, Oliver was desperate with hunger, and reckless with misery. He rose from the table; and walking to the master, basin and spoon in hand,
said, 'Please, sir, I want some more.'
    The master was a fat, healthy man; but he turned very pale. He gazed in astonishment

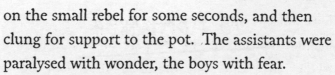

on the small rebel for some seconds, and then clung for support to the pot. The assistants were paralysed with wonder, the boys with fear.

'What.' said the master at length, in a faint voice.

'Please, sir,' replied Oliver, 'I want some more.'

I could just picture it. Not that I have ever lived in a workhouse of course. Dear Albert says that Charles Dickens was writing to attack the laws that Uncle King William passed. The 'Poor Laws'.

He says the law was there to make people work. The paupers who have no money must go to the Workhouse. But the Workhouse is such a bleak place – and the food so awful – the poor will do everything they can to stay out. Husbands and wives are sent to separate parts to do awful jobs and infants are sent to baby farms.

But Albert says the paupers are so disgusting that is all they deserve. Another writer said that one night he gave a feast for 30 beggars in a slum boarding-house . . .

The dinner was then divided out into twenty-five platefuls, all the plates that the boarding house owned. It was handed out through a small window in the kitchen. As he hurried to the seat behind the bare table, a pauper would start to tear the meat apart with his fingers for knives and forks were unknown here. A beggar boy whirled the plate round on his thumb as he went. Then, dipping his nose in the plate, seized a potato in his mouth.

But in Andover Workhouse the 61-year-old Samuel Green told an inspector what happened when fresh bones arrived. The paupers were given bones to strip the meat from. Some ATE the meat raw, the disgusting beasts.

Samuel Green

An inspector wrote ...

> I have seen them take a bone from the dung heap and chew it while reeking hot with decay. Bones which still had thin strips of flesh sticking to them, they scraped carefully with their knives and put the bits, no matter how befouled with dirt, into a pocket. They have told me that, whether in broth or grilled, they were the most savoury dish that could be imagined. These creatures are often hardly human in appearance, they have no human tastes or understanding, nor even human feelings, for they enjoy the filth which we expect to see in dogs and other lower animals.

But that inspector was a fool. I am sure MOST of the paupers are happy that they are not starving. Look at dear old Samuel Green who seemed VERY happy with the place.

I like the fresh bones – I never touched one that was a little rotten; the marrow was as good as the meat. It was all covered over by bone; that was when they were fresh and good.

The allowance of potatoes at dinner is half a pound, but we used to get nearly a pound, seven or eight middling sized potatoes. The food we got in the workhouse was very good; I could not wish for better, all I wanted was a little more. I have seen a man named Reeves eat horse-flesh off the bones.

So, you see? The workhouse is not so bad after all, and Mr Dickens is writing about a boy who does not exist. It is just a story. The Oliver Twist book is simply good fun.

15 August 1839

Today, my diary, a new law said letters can be sent to anywhere in Britain for one penny.

One of my subjects, Rowland Hill, invented the postage stamp. Letter-writers can now buy a small square of paper to stick on their letter sheet. For some reason it is known as a 'penny black'.

Anyway, Mr Hill wanted a picture to go on the stamp. He asked if he could use a picture of ME.

'Oh, dear,' I cried, surely you should use the picture of a beautiful woman?' And he said that is exactly why he said he wanted me. Silly man. I have to say I do look rather pretty. Pretty as a picture. (My joke).

The writers must lick the back of my head to stick the stamp on their envelope. That is NOT such a nice thought.

Mr Hill then went on to arrange a postal service. He has an idea for pillar boxes on street corners, where people can 'post' their letters and doors on every house must have 'letter boxes' to take them. All very clever.

The men who carry the letters are called 'postmen' and they wear bright red jackets. The people in the street call the postmen 'Robin Redbreasts'.

MUST DASH OR I'LL GET THE SACK!

The postman at Buckingham Palace leaves the letters at the servants' hall and I went there this morning to tell cook about a special dinner tonight.

Just as I walked in the kitchen a footman was shouting a disgraceful poem after the postman about a robin redbreast.

A robin redbreast on my sill
sang for a crust of bread,
I slowly brought the window down
and smashed its bloomin' head!

He turned and saw me and I though he was going to faint with shock. He knew I should sack him there and then for such an awful verse. But, my secret diary, I couldn't. I had a handkerchief in front of my mouth and had to bite it because I was trying not to laugh. It was a VERY funny poem.

I feel better now. I shall call my butler and tell him to sack the footman.

10 February 1840

The adorable angel Albert of Saxe Coburg and Gotha wants to marry me. On 15 October last year I proposed to him.

I wanted to marry him then and there. But it takes time for a country to plan the wedding of its queen.

Today, three months later, we married in the Chapel Royal at St James's Palace. We make a wonderfully handsome couple.

I do like a bit of CAKE!

My British people will be so pleased to see a happy royal family after the royals they remember.

For years they had Grandfather George III and he was a little odd. His wife Charlotte was so ugly the crowds thought she looked like a dog and shouted 'Pug' as she drove through the streets.

Charlotte

Of course she was German so she didn't understand the joke. 'What are they saying? She asked (in German).

And her servants said, 'They are shouting God Save The Queen.'

No wonder the British people love me - not odd or ugly or lazy or dull.

Britain's Prince Charmless who used to tell lies. He said that he had led a great charge

at the Battle of Waterloo when, really, he
was tucked up in bed in London.

He wanted to marry his lady-friend the
actress Maria Fitzherbert. She wasn't so
sure about him. So, he said he would kill
himself if she didn't marry him. He pretended
to stab himself - but his doctor probably
just made a little nick in his side before
Maria arrived. The trick worked; she promised
to marry him on the spot.

But Maria was a Catholic. Members of
Parliament were horrified when they heard
the future queen was a Catholic. They
wanted him to marry his German cousin,
Caroline.

Caroline

George refused. The MPs knew that George owed a lot of people a lot of money. The MPs offered him a lot of money IF he would give up his lady friend and marry Caroline instead. Your money . . . or your wife?

What did Prince George do? He agreed to marry Caroline and give up Maria. Then they spent the rest of their lives hating one another.

And King Uncle William was just as bad. His lady-friend was an actress they called Mrs Jordan. They had ten children. Again, he was forced to marry a princess - that was Adelaide. At least he liked her. Adelaide is dull as ditch-water and will only be remembered because they gave her name to a town in Australia.

But you can see why my people will be glad to have a marriage of two loving hearts. Albert, my angel, and me. We shall rule wisely and well.

Some of my people, trouble-makers called Chartists, want common people to have votes and rule themselves. My ministers refused and the Chartists ran riot in Birmingham on our wedding day. Of course, it led to tragedy. My newspaper made sad reading.

Chartists riot in Newport, Wales
Today a crowd of angry Chartists gathered in Newport carrying weapons. Troops were sent in to force the crowd to go home. When they refused the troops fired into the crowd and 22 died.

Oh dear. Those foolish people have ME and Albert to rule them. I do hope there will be no more nonsense of this kind.

The rebel leaders will be transported to Australia and I hope they learn their lesson.

Mind you, Australia in becoming a problem. Convicts escaped from there to New Zealand and made trouble for the native Maori people. It is best if we buy the land from the Maoris and rule it.

My ministers plan to do the same Canada, South Africa and West Africa. We are already the greatest traders in India. We are building quite a large empire.

10 August 1842

If I am going to be the greatest queen in the world then sadly some people will die fighting for me. But I can also use my great power to save a lot of lives too.

The reports are coming in about the deaths of my soldiers in the Afghan War back in January.

As you know Russia is what we in Britain call 'The Enemy'. And we are struggling with them to rule the countries north of India. The struggle we call 'The Great Game'. It is a game I must win if I want to make my empire even bigger.

My gentlemen soldiers fight on horses, while the common soldiers fight on foot. The gentlemen even took a pack of foxhounds to Afghanistan so they could hunt when they weren't fighting. All part of the Great Game – unless you are a fox. (My little joke). Many took their wives ... a terrible mistake if you ask me.

I gave the command to old General William Elphinstone. The poor dear had gout and carried his arm in a sling. He could not walk, and he couldn't ride. He had to be carried everywhere in a chair, for goodness sake. And ... I'm sorry, it has to be said ... his mind was becoming rather weak.

Elphinstone

The Afghan tribes did not want us in their
land. I do not know why. But the tribes
marched into Kabul and murdered our governor
and all his staff while General William's army
sat in a fortress outside the city.

Our troops looked very smart but, sadly, they
were rotten shots. They were so busy building
forts and marching about they never took
the time to practice useful little skills like
firing a musket. When the Afghans attacked
my troops fired ... and missed. Some of my
officers even tried to throw stones at the
Afghans to drive them back.

My army threw away their weapons and ran
away back to the fortress. But at least they
lived to fight another day.

General William decided it was time to get
back to the safety of India. It was suicide.
I have seen pictures of those mountains in
winter. The only way to travel is through the
passes. The lowest pass is 10,000 feet. The

highest mountain in Britain is Ben Nevis. It is not even 5,000 feet. My army had to climb, carrying food, while slowed down by women and children.

It was January and the snow was over a foot deep. People were dying of the cold before our gallant army even reached that dreadful pass. Of course, the Afghans knew that. They simply waited for us in the Khyber Pass and attacked. It was not war, it was a massacre. Poor old General William was wounded in the fighting. But not a glorious death – he was hit in the backside. His body was found and carried in a coffin. But he was not allowed to rest in peace. The coffin carriers were attacked, the coffin torn open and Elphinstone's body pelted with stones.

An officer reported the natives were like savages...

The Afghans fought fiercely and after shooting an enemy down they'd move in to

carve up the body ... even if the enemy was still alive. Now, it is not very pleasant being chopped up while you are still alive. The Afghan women followed the warriors to strip the bodies of anything valuable. The army's Indian servants were stripped of all their clothing and left alive to freeze to death in the snow.

Some soldiers believed it was better to shoot themselves rather than be taken alive in Afghanistan.

Only Dr. William Brydon and a handful of Indian soldiers survived to tell the tale. Lady Butler painted his image.

Lady Butler painting

Sixteen thousand died – shot, stabbed, frozen to death – in these mountain passes – as Brydon said, 'the slaughter was tremendous'. The Great Game may cost lives but when you play games you expect to lose the odd match. I shall win in the end.

Now, the good news is I signed a new law today that will SAVE lives. The 'Mines Act' says that boys under the age of 10, women and girls, may no longer work down the mines. It was dangerous and disgusting work, they say. I have seen the pictures and read the reports.

I am not sure what those children will DO all day when their parents go off to work. If the parents have money, they can pay a school dame to teach the children. The problem is the parents will have NO money because the children will have no wages. Such a shame. But I am sure someone will come up with an idea to keep the children of the poor doing something useful.

I am so happy that I could sign this new law and make the little children happy.

And what makes me happy is travelling on the new railways. I am the first ruler of Britain to go by train. So exciting. This year I have visited Scotland for the first time and hope to go there by train someday. The countryside is wonderful. Sadly, the towns of

Glasgow and Edinburgh are full of slums. A report said...

Glasgow is possibly the filthiest and unhealthiest of all British towns. The passageways that link the tenements are little more than open sewers. It is no surprise that half of the children die before the age of five.

Edwin Chadwick

I shall go to Balmoral Castle and stay away from those dreadful city slums.

30 March 1843

My British people are so very clever. This month the Brunels' tunnel was opened to allow people to cross UNDER the River Thames. How amazing.

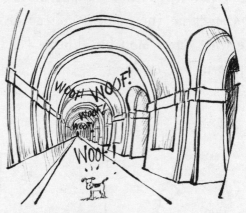

It was built by Mr Marc Brunel (who came from France) and his son, Isambard (who is British really). Isambard built the railway line from London to Bristol.

I saw the tunnel and said that Mr Brunel's train could travel under the ground of

London. Mr Brunel said that was a wonderful idea and went away to see if it could be done. I think I have just invented something as clever as my great British inventors.

And last month I saw plans from Sir George Cayley. He has been building gliding planes for many years. But now he has a plan for a powered machine they call a helicopter. Imagine. One day I may be able to fly to my holiday home in Scotland.

Sir George Cayley

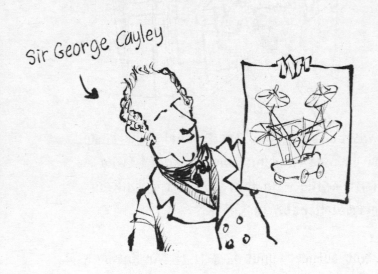

21 November 1845

I am hearing reports from Ireland that say the potato crops have been ruined.

The little farmers lived on potatoes. The peasants had no money, but they had their potatoes. The most popular type of potato was 'lumper' or 'horse potato'. It grew on poorest land and gave huge crop.

You just plant your potatoes in April and May, pick them in August, then they can be stored and eaten until the following May.

During summer, your family has to buy oatmeal to eat until next crop of potatoes

– they called this 'summer hunger' but it was not too bad.

Then, this September 1845, a disease attacked the potatoes and it spread quickly over the country. When the farmers pulled them up, the potatoes were black and rotten inside.

The people had no money to buy food and they began to starve.

I suppose they must be used to going hungry. Some people are. Some people (like me) are not. There is a writer and a member of Parliament called Benjamin Disraeli who said my people are not one nation ... they are TWO nations. This strange man wrote ...

There are two nations between whom there is no talking and no sympathy; who are as ignorant of each other's habits, thoughts, and feelings, as if they lived in different zones, or inhabitants of different planets. The rich and the poor.

I suppose that is what Mr James Greenwood found when he explored the poor people in the cities of Britain.

I have note of three or four streets, where 48 men, 73 women, and 59 children are living in thirty-four rooms. When I visited the back room of No. 5, I found it occupied by one man, two women, and two children; and in it was the dead body of a poor girl who had died a few days before. The body was stretched out on the bare floor, without a sheet or coffin. There it lay in the middle of the living, and such sights as these are common.

My heart is sorry for the Irish and the poor.

10 April 1848

What a year of terror this has been. All over Europe rebels have risen up and thrown out their kings and lords. In this country the Chartists called for a meeting to march on Parliament. They had a petition to hand in to my ministers and they said six million people had signed it.

But it was laughed at because some of the names were tom-foolery. They had signed:

Pugnose

Queen Victoria

MrPunch.

Bread and cheese

Lord Wellin

My Lord Wellington was in charge of my defence. I was sent from London to be safe. There were cannon at the gates of Buckingham Palace and boats on the Thames ready to bring in troops if they were needed.

The offices of my government had their doors blocked with piles of books, which sounds a little odd, but it worked. Those ruined rulers of Europe should have taken a leaf out of my book. (Ha-ha).

It is all so dangerous and thrilling in a way. Wellington is nearly 80, but a strong, sensible man. He made 170,000 common people constables for the day. 200,000 Chartists were expected to meet at Kennington. Only about 20,000 turned up. My bishops prayed for my safety and God heard their prayers.

Chartists

He sent heavy rain and the miserable marchers just went back home to get dry. Chartism is dead, my ministers say. Some of the Chartists wanted votes for women. That will never happen. Some want revolution, like France. That will never happen because my people love me too much.

12 August 1849

Today sees the end of our visit to Ireland to see my poor, poor starving people.

My ministers showed me reports from visitors that filled me with horror. I once read a book by that awful Mary Shelley called 'Frankenstein'. I was shocked that a woman could write such a disgusting tale. But the trues stories from Ireland were worse.

An American woman called Asanath Nicholson went to Ireland to give out free Bibles ... I do not know why she bothered, because most peasants cannot read. But she was shocked by what she saw.

I was told of a cabin where in a dark corner lay a family of father, mother and two children lying together. The father was considerably rotted, whilst the mother had died last and had fastened the door so

63

that their bodies would not be seen. Such family scenes were quite common' The cabin was simply pulled down over the corpses as a grave.

We crossed to a small island near Donegal in a boat and found it deserted. All we could see were dogs. I wondered, 'How can the dogs look so fat and shining here, where there is no food for the people.' Then the pilot of my boat told her what dogs were eating.

The misery was recorded by people like William Carleton who wrote a book The Black Prophet ...

The roads were black with funerals and, as you passed from village to village, the death bells were ringing forth in slow and gloomy tones. They were ringing a triumph of Death over the face of our country - a country that was filled with darker and deeper sadness every day.

I decided I must visit my Irish people. My ministers said the Irish were angry with me because the great land-owners are all cruel and English. Some Irish peasants revolted and killed their landlords.

Many English land-owners tried to help by paying the fares of the hungry families to sail to America. But the journey could be a nightmare and many failed to make it. The ships became known as 'Coffin Ships'. An officer from one of the ships wrote:

SS Elizabeth and Sarah sailed from Mayo in July 1846 for Canada. She held 276 emigrants. There was not enough water. Every passenger was allowed three kilos of food each week, but none was given out. There were no toilets. The Captain got lost, and the voyage lasted 8 weeks. 42 people died before this 'coffin ship' docked in Canada.

But I am no coward. Albert and the children and I sailed to Cork on 2 August and ended our tour today. I can only say I was amazed at how much love they showed me. Crowds of pale and ragged people cheered us wherever we went waving hats and handkerchiefs.

Bands played. I wore a dress with a pattern of shamrocks, the Irish flower, and they loved that.

We feel so deeply touched.

We were greeted with banners that showed their love.

Before the famine I had eight million Irish subjects. After five years of the famine and disease there are just six and a half million. I hope the living will find happiness.

I told Albert that when we return to London, I shall give £2000 to help the poor and starving. Albert, my clever husband, said that this would give each Irish person a quarter of a quarter of a penny.

NEVER MIND. AT LEAST I AM DOING SOMETHING.

11 September 1849

Albert and I are having a holiday at Balmoral Castle in Scotland. The servants here are really charming.

A boy called John Brown leads my pony and he is the finest young Scotsman you could ever meet. He looks so smart in his kilt. Charming, really charming. And the other servants are pleasant too.

Albert

Balmoral

Kestrel

Craig Liadh

John Brown

Pony POO!

27 September 1849

Today should have been a great day. I arrived in Newcastle-upon-Tyne to open a new bridge. That does NOT sound exciting. But this was a bridge that would carry trains across the River Tyne.

Before this High Level Bridge was built I had to get off the train on the south of the river and take a carriage across on a low level bridge and take another train on the North side. When Mr Stephenson's bridge over the River Tweed is finished next year, I will be able to travel from Buckingham Palace to my summer holidays in Balmoral without changing trains or leaving my carriage.

The High Level bridge is a wonder. Trains cross the top and there is a road for carriages, carts and walkers underneath.

Stephenson →

69

It was planned by the wonderful Robert Stephenson – the son of the clever George Stephenson who has built so many railway lines. When I was born 30 years ago there were no railways. Now they spread across Britain like a spider's web. See Mr Carter's map.

Railway Lines

It is just 20 years since the first passenger line opened.

I am a lover of rail travel but am a nervous passenger. I have told my drivers that no matter how fast engines CAN run MY train will not do more than 40 mph.

I was saying that this should have been a great day. After the opening there was to be a fine meal at the Station Hotel in Newcastle. I cannot believe what happened next.

The manager of the hotel – a weedy little ferret of a man with a moustache like a hairy slug came up to my table with a piece of paper in his hand. He pushed it towards me. What was it? It was a bill for the meal.

I still cannot believe it. I am so angry with Newcastle-upon-Tyne I shall never look upon this city ever again. When my train travels to and from Balmoral I shall pull the curtains closed as we pass through this town.

How dare ferret-face?
HOW DARE HE?

1 May 1851

Today the Great Exhibition opened at the beautiful Crystal Palace. It was the idea of my wonderful husband, but I had a lot to do with making it happen. (Yes, I know, some people say it was a man called Henry Cole who wanted Britain to copy a great French Exhibition of seven years ago. But it would not have happened without my Albert driving it forward.)

It is a show of all that Britain does so well. The science, the arts, the trade, the industry. And look at the palace of glass they built to show it in.

I opened it, of course, with my Albert by my side. Oh, how the crowds loved me. They came in their thousands on one of Britain's greatest wonders - the railways.

The poet, Mr Thackeray wrote of the wonderful Crystal Palace...

Thackeray

As though it was by a wizard's wand,
As blazing arch of clearest glass,
Leaps like a fountain from the grass,
To meet the sun.

The things I remember were the huge steam hammer, adding machines, carpets, ribbons, printing machines, musical instruments, carriages, bicycles, farm machines, guns and watches.

The famous Koh-i-Noor diamond was put on show. It is the largest diamond in the world. My brave soldiers brought it back from India when we won the Sikh War two years ago. Albert had it cut to make a brooch. He says one day it may fit my crown. Dear Albert.

The Koh-i-Noor diamond was shown inside a glass safe inside a golden bird cage so the

75

common people could see it. They can look but they cannot touch as it is their queen's precious jewel.

Koh!

I Nooo!

I do feel badly that we stole it from an Indian prince – my soldiers said they would kill his mother if he did not hand it over – but that is what happens when you lose a war.

The most popular sights were the factory machines in action. One showed how we take raw cotton and see it being spun into thread then woven into cloth using looms.

The workers look so clean and happy and

safe and fresh. I do know that it is not like that in the real mills, even though we have set the children free.

There are accidents I have read about:

> On the 6th of March a very sad accident happened to a lad named Joseph Foden about 13 years of age. While sweeping under a machine his head was caught between the Roller beam and the carriage and completely smashed, death being instant.
>
> Quarry Bank Mill record

The pay is poor, and the punishments are harsh. One boy in a nail-making factory was punished for making useless nails by having his head laid down on a counter. And then, a report said ...

> The boy had a nail hammered through his ear, and the boy has made good nails ever since.

Children of 10 years still work in the factories and are bullied. Punishments were part of the life of the factory child. One inspector said ...

> *The brutal overlookers will often beat them cruelly, and I have seen them strike the children, knocking them off their stools and sending them spinning several feet on the greasy floor.*
>
> *Samuel Fielden*

The blazing Crystal Palace arch of clearest glass cost a lot of money and some mean people complained. It is the biggest glass building the world has ever seen. All the glass together is 84,000 metres square, they tell me. I cannot imagine that, but it is what I call 'a lot'. Sadly, the glass costs money and human struggles to make.

> *Like millworkers, children who worked in glass-making faced serious injuries and deaths every day. Bosses sneered at these*

'dog boys' or 'blower's dogs'—because they were trained to follow the adult glass blower's whistle.

The children handled and cleaned every piece of scalding, liquid glass that the glass blower took from the furnace. They worked as fast as they could and paid the price for being too fast and careless.

In one accident, a 14-year-old boy was blinded in one eye after being struck by a piece of flying glass. 'Blow-overs,' or glass dust, caused extreme pain once it got into the lungs or the eyes. Burns and dried bodies were common of course, but so were lung diseases like tuberculosis and pneumonia. This was caused by working in great heat and then walking home on a cold winter night.

Report 1850

But those gallant dog boys who died will be happy in heaven. They will know that they died to make our Exhibition great.

11 November 1853

What are we to do? Australia was a perfect place to send our criminals. It is on the other side of the world and there is a lot of hard work to make the convicts sweat. But now Australia has decided it wants no more convicts. What on earth will we do with them.

On 13 May 1787 – 66 years ago – we sent the first lot of villains. The youngest rogue was John Hudson, a nine-year old chimney sweep. There were not a lot of chimneys in Australia in those days.

The oldest was Dorothy Handland and her job in England had been a rag dealer. Dorothy was 88 years old and it is amazing she lasted that journey of 36 weeks. Others were not so lucky. 48 of the other convicts had died on the journey - which may be better than living in Australia.

Some were punished on the ships for bad behaviour with 300, 400 or 800 lashes on the back.

Many were held in chains or behind bars for the whole journey. Children were not supposed to be transported till they were 14 but one boy was sent there at the age of 6. It was said he could hardly talk properly.

But how could you punish a really rotten convict who kept breaking the laws - a sort of 'super-convict'?

Send him (or her) to a large island to the south of the mainland: Tasmania - just dump the convicts on the island and let them wander round to live or die. These wandering criminals were known as 'Bushrangers' and they brought terror to the natives of Tasmania ... the Aborigines. The bushrangers

killed the aborigines as if it were a game.

A witness reported ...

One bushranger, known as Carrots, killed an aborigine man. Then he seized the dead man's wife. He cut off the man's head and fastened it round the wife's neck. Then he drove the weeping woman off to his den to be his slave.

They say that soon there will be no aborigines left in Terrible Tasmania.

SOMETIMES MY EMPIRE CAN BE HARD ON THE NATIVES.

20 September 1854

I have a brooch made with the Koh-i-noor diamond, but I think I shall not wear it again. You see, they say it is cursed.

It was dug up many years ago but has brought bad luck to many of the people who have handled it.

We took it from the Indian prince and brought it to Britain in a ship. The ship was struck by dreadful storms. But, worse, the crew fell sick with cholera and many died.

And now cholera is visiting Britain again. Nine hundred people have died horribly from this cursed disease. Six years ago in 1848 over 12,000 died in London alone. Mostly poor people. They even wrote a letter to The Times newspaper to complain.

We live in muck and filth. We ain't got no toilets, no dust bins, no water splies or no drain in the whole place. If the colera comes Lord help us.

And now it has come. My doctor explained...

A person with cholera has endless watery poo that smells of fish. They vomit and their heart beats fast while their mouth and their skin are dry.
The victim loses around 10-20 litres of fluid from their body each day, so they dry out. Due to this rapid water loss your kidneys pack up, the salts in your blood become dangerously low. The amount of blood in your body falls. This gives you a blue-grey colour to your skin, but then you die.

Doctor Snow

Doctors have always said that cholera is carried in the air and on bad smells. But a brilliant doctor called John Snow said it is carried in water - water in sewers carries the disease. If only we had known that before.

Doctor Snow drew a map of where the disease was killing people in West London. The dots showed the deaths and you could see they came in clumps ...

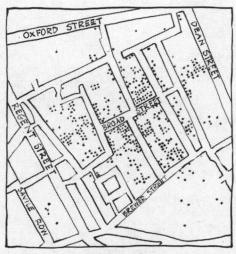

Doctor Snow's Cholera map

He wrote about his amazing discovery ...

Within 250 yards of the spot where Cambridge Street joins Broad Street there were more than of 500 deadly attacks of cholera in 10 days. I believed some disease was getting of the water of the much-frequented street-pump in Broad Street.

The sewers had leaked into the pump water. What did John do? He took the handle off the pump so no one could use it again till the leaking sewers were fixed. No one in Broad Street has died from cholera since.

In Buckingham Palace we have fresh water, of course. One day even the poorest of my people will all have fresh water, then they may not smell so badly.

Clever Doctor Snow. But I will still not wear my Koh-i-noor diamond again.

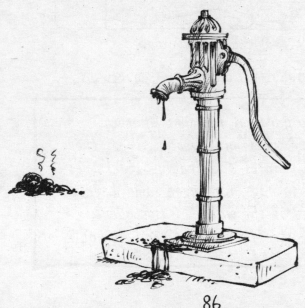

4 November 1854

We are at war again. We have to be. The Russians are trying to build an Empire and it is Britain's job to stop them. We will put an end to their plans at a place called The Crimea.

We have had tragedies already. My horse soldiers, the Light Brigade, were given the wrong orders and charged straight at the Russian canon. They were blown away. Those poor horses.

The ordinary soldiers have been suffering and dying of disease as well as wounds. In the hospitals they were lying on dirty floors two weeks before they got to see a doctor. Those floors are crawling with rats and insects. The men had no beds, and some had no blankets or pillows – they rested their heads on their boots. There were no toilets just 20 chamber pots for 1000 men in one hospital and the pots overflow.

All that will change. I have sent a woman to sort out the mess. Her name is Florence Nightingale and she will arrive today with almost 40 nurses to help.

Men make wars but we women patch them up.

I have decided to create a new medal for the bravest of my fighters. I shall call it the Victoria Cross.

8 September 1857

Children can be a problem. Not MY children. I mean the children of the poor. The law does not allow young children to work so they wander the streets and get into trouble. A new law called 'The Industrial Schools Act' gives these children schools to keep then off the streets.

The little paupers are trained to be hard working and given a trade they can do when they leave.

The law says ...

The following children shall be sent to an Industrial School:

- any child under 14 caught begging

- any child found wandering homeless

- any child found with a gang of thieves

- any child under 12 who has committed a crime

- any child under 14 whose parents say s/he is out of control

The boarding schools (where they stay) start at 6:00am and go on till bedtime at 7:00pm.

During the day there are lessons in religion, reading, writing, eating, and learning skills. The lucky children even have with three breaks for play. The boys do gardening, tailoring, and shoemaking; the girls learn housework and washing, knitting, and sewing.

Mr Dickens said that some children are too shabby even for Industrial Schools. They go to a Ragged School:

Dickens described the Ragged Schools. He wrote a letter to 'The Daily News'

Those who are too ragged, wretched, filthy, and forlorn, to enter any other place: invited

to come in here and find some people willing to teach them something.

I visited one Ragged School with two or three miserable rooms, upstairs in a miserable house. In the best of these, the pupils in the girls' school were being taught to read and write. The appearance of this room was sad but there was some hope. The room next door was a worse place.

The narrow, low space at the back was so foul and stifling as to be almost unbearable. Huddled together on a bench about the room were a crowd of boys.

They were aged from mere infants to young men; sellers of fruit, herbs, matches, flints; sleepers under the dry arches of bridges; young thieves and beggars.

Mr Dickens thinks the rich people of the cities should pay for better schools for the poor. Good, kind Mr Dickens. I wish him luck.

25 September 1857

I am sad to hear that not all of the people in India want my brave troops there. We have 40,000 soldiers and they rule with the help of 230,000 native troops – Sepoys.

Sepoy

On 10 May the native troops rebelled, but the cowards waited till the British were in church then they massacred our brave lads, as well as the British women and children.

Now word has come that Indian rebels led by Nana Sahib have taken 3200 British prisoners, hacked them to death and thrown the pieces down a well.

The British revenge shall be terrible, they say. Our army will capture rebels and make them clean up the blood from their massacre — if they refuse they will be lashed and made to lick it up.

Some rebel leaders have been tied across the mouth of a canon and then it is set off. British ladies have been splashed with the blood and smiled.

War is terrible but India needs our strong rule.

India has been ruled by the traders, The East India Company, to deal in cotton, silk, salt, spices, and of course tea. But they have allowed the Indian people to starve when famines struck. It is time Britain closed down

The East India Company and we rule India from London as part of our growing empire.

I think of the empire as my crown. India shall be the jewel in my crown. Just like the Koh-i-noor.

23 December 1861

Today is the saddest day of my life. Today I buried my greatest love, my Albert. Oh, I know we quarrelled a lot and disagreed on many things. But I shall miss him helping me to rule my wonderful lands that are beginning to stretch around the world.

In fact, little British Isles are ruling over an empire. I should be an Empress, not just a queen. I shall see about that when I settle into my new life as a widow. I shall wear black. Albert's clothes shall be laid out in his bedroom as they were when he was alive.

My Albert died on 14 December at Windsor Castle. The doctors say he died of typhoid – like so many of the starving Irish ten years ago. As Albert lay in his sick-bed I asked the doctor to tell me what this disease was. He explained.

It starts with a week of fever, cough and generally feeling poorly. By the second week the fever is really high and you can do nothing but lie in bed. You have fevered dreams, with red spots on your belly. You enter the third week of illness for the start of the diarrhoea. Green diarrhoea, like pea soup. Your body is losing water.
That makes your heart and your bowel bursts and poisons your blood. You become exhausted and with all your organs shutting down you die.

Doctor ↑

I rather wish I had not asked him.

A great prince should 'lie in state' - his body put on display in church so people can walk past and look at him one last time. We decided Albert would NOT lie in state. It would take too much time and we wanted him buried before Christmas. How Albert used to love Christmas. He brought his German ideas to Britain - Christmas Trees with candles

were his idea, of course. Aunt Charlotte brought one across from Germany first about fifty years ago.

Doctor Watkins was there and described Charlotte's tree, put up for the children of the palace workers:

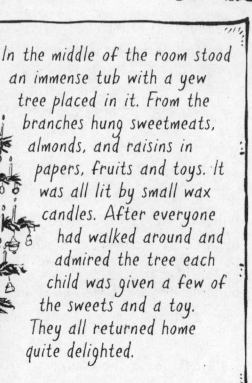

In the middle of the room stood an immense tub with a yew tree placed in it. From the branches hung sweetmeats, almonds, and raisins in papers, fruits and toys. It was all lit by small wax candles. After everyone had walked around and admired the tree each child was given a few of the sweets and a toy. They all returned home quite delighted.

The idea of Christmas trees did not become popular till my Albert had one put up forty years after Charlotte's lonesome pine. I remember my excited husband wrote to his father ...

Today I have two children of my own who are full of happy wonder at the German Christmas tree and its shimmering candles.

So, Albert will miss Christmas. Or at least he will spend this Christmas in the cold grave at Windsor. His remains were taken to a funeral building at Frogmore, near Windsor. In time I shall be buried alongside him. It is a fine building and what we call a mausoleum ... such a gloomy word I always think.

I did not go to the church service. Women these days are not popular at funerals because they cry and faint too much. I would not do that, but I was happy to stay in Windsor Castle.

The powerful men of Ireland refused to come to the funeral. They call me the Famine Queen. Me? After I gave £2000 of my own money to help them. I shall spend my time in Scotland, not Ireland, when I want a holiday. But enough of this gloom. I shall have to go on and become the greatest queen in the world without the help of my dear Albert.

HAPPY CHRISTMAS, ALBERT.

10 January 1863

Today's London Underground Railway opened. I do not tell everyone that it was my idea. They all think it was invented by Charles Pearson and planned John Fowler. But Pearson died last year and never saw this opening. So, he cannot argue if I say it was my idea.

The trains are pulled by steam trains, so they are very smoky.

I would not travel on one. Someone has said underground trains will be powered by electric in years to come. But that is silly. How can they get an electric cable long enough? Trust me, electric trains will never happen.

Of course, some slum houses had to be flattened to allow the tunnels to be built. I do not know where the common people from those houses will go but I am sure they will find somewhere. It is what they are used to. A man from Russia came to London and wrote ...

Every night there are 100,000 people in London who do not know where they will lay their heads. And the police often find women and children dead from hunger.

Russian Man

Even the dead people have no rest. Ten years ago, the law stopped people being buried in London City. Graveyards were becoming too crowded; coffins sometimes jutted out of grounds and the air filled with a dreadful stench.

Up to 20 poor people could be buried in the same grave. Grave-diggers sometimes jumped up and down on the bodies to cram them in.

Some people have blamed the old graveyards for causing cholera. Many have been cleared of gravestones to make way for the railways — but they have often left the human remains under the tracks.

The Underground digging has now disturbed other graveyards. I read a letter to The Standard newspaper that complained ...

Sir,

I wish to complain about the way some human remains have been treated while the underground line at Saint Pancras station is built.

A workman told me that bones from St Pancras churchyard were dug up and were stuffed into one of the railway trucks.

A clerk for the railway company watched the work and even wrote a poem. His name is Mr Thomas Hardy.

We late-lamented, resting here,
Are mixed to human jam,
And each to each exclaims in fear,
'I know not which I am!'

Human jam? Is this any way to treat the dead?

I shall be buried at Winsor alongside Albert. No one can disturb our peaceful rest.

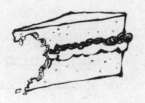

20 June 1867

My people have been having parties to remember that I have been on the throne for 30 years.

Not all of the Street entertainment is very pleasant

The Hyde Park Fair had some STRANGE and NASTY amusements ...

The Hyde Park Fair

1 Week from 20 June 1867

See:

Talented Pigs

Pony Fortune Teller

Fattest Man

2 Headed Lady

Living Skeleton

Spottiest Boys

Pig Faced Lady

105

The Pig-faced Lady – was especially sad. It was a bear that had its face and paws shaved to look like pink skin. The paws were laced into padded gloves and the animal strapped to a chair with a table in front of it.

Then the performance began. The bear was asked questions. A boy prodded it with a stick after each question. The bear grunted and that seemed to be a reply ...

Can you BEAR-LIEVE it!

Are you 18 years old? (Prod – Grunt.)

Is it true you were born in Preston in Lancashire? (Prod – Grunt.)

Are you well and happy? (Prod – Grunt.)

Are you planning to get married? (Prod – Grunt.)

I WILL MAKE SURE THE WHOLE THING IS BANNED.

26 May 1868

I am bothered by the execution of Michael Barrett, an Irish traitor, this morning. I am not bothered by the hanging, of course. As the Bible says, 'An eye for an eye and a tooth for a tooth'. Barrett was one of six men who planted a bomb they are calling The Clerkenwell Explosion. They were trying to blow a hole in the walls of Clerkenwell Prison to set their Irish traitor friends free. Irish traitors who had shot a policeman dead a month ago.

They did great damage and killed 12 innocent people. One was a little girl. Fifty more were injured. Poor houses were blown apart and families left without a home. I saw the shocking scene myself last December.

It was a new Gunpowder Plot and the Irish did better than Guy Fawkes. A barrel of

black gunpowder had been placed on the end of a street seller's barrow and wheeled to the wall of the prison. They knew that the prisoners would be exercising in the yard on the other side of the wall. The wall was blown down but no prisoners escaped.

Michael Barrett said ...

> *I love my country and if it is murderous to love Ireland dearer than I love my life, then it is true, I am a murderer.*

But he said he did not plant the gunpowder. He said he was in Glasgow at the time and people said they saw him there. He may have been innocent. I am not bothered by that.

But I AM bothered that only one man was hanged for this dreadful crime. In future Irish rebels should be hanged as soon as they are arrested. They do not need a trial. In America I believe they call this 'lynching'.

Barrett was hanged by my excellent hangman, William Calcraft. Calcraft is very fast. Albert would say he doesn't hang around. (I miss Albert's merry jests).

Barrett was executed this morning OUTSIDE Newgate Prison.

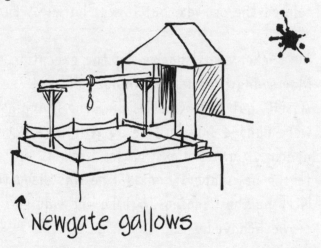

↑ Newgate gallows

Two THOUSAND people turned up to watch and to sing 'Rule Britannia'. That is how popular hanging in public is. But in three days' time it will be banned. In future people will be hanged INSIDE the prison where no one but the guards and priest can see them.

I blame Charles Dickens. Yes, he is a great writer and he made Christmas a great event when he wrote his tales of Scrooge and Tiny Tim: 'A Christmas carol'. But why did he have to interfere with the execution of killers? Yes, as Calcraft went to work there were comic songs and laughing while pick-pockets robbed the crowds, but it was harmless fun.

Mr Dickens was shocked by the execution of Maria and Fredrick Manning. I did not see it myself, but dear Charles did. The Mannings were hanged side by side by William Calcraft nearly 20 years ago. Charles Dickens wrote to the newspapers and said he was disgusted NOT by the hangings, but by the way the crowd behaved.

I was a witness of the execution at Horsemonger Lane this morning. I saw an awful and wicked sight with the crowd out to enjoy themselves.

People became ashamed to go to a hanging for some pleasure. My people need to SEE what will happen if they break my laws.

Of course, the Irish are furious. The rebels call themselves 'Fenians'. I have had many letters saying they will kill me. I have so many guards I am a prisoner myself. How can that be fair?

30 March 1869

I had news today that a man they call King Billy has died. He was the last native man from Tasmania left alive.

King Billy

It seems the evil convicts - Bushrangers - that we sent to Australia have killed off all 20,000 natives in just 80 years.

The Royal College of Surgeons in England (MY college of Surgeons, I should call it) wanted parts of Tasmania's last man to study. (They are a little like the body-snatchers who roamed the land in the days of Uncle King William.)

Tasmania refused to allow my surgeons to have the corpse, so surgeon William Crowther broke into where the corpses were kept, removed King Billy's skull, and sent it back to England. It was theft. Skullduggery, in fact, I joked to my lady-in-waiting.

Crowther removed King Billy's skin and put a skull from a white body into the black skin so the doctors in Tasmania would not notice. When they found out, the Tasmanian doctors cut off King Billy's hands and feet, so the body was worthless. They buried the rest of Billy's bits.

A WICKED THING TO DO, I SUPPOSE. I DO BELIEVE A LOT OF HISTORY IS HORRIBLE.

9 June 1870

Poor Mr Dickens, my great writer, has died in Rochester. He was just 58. No age at all. They say that he was exhausted by fame. But I know the truth.

I love the railways, but they finished for poor Charles. Exactly five years ago he was in a rail crash at Staplehurst in Kent, England. Ten passengers died and forty more were injured.

The railway line was being repaired at a spot where it ran over a low bridge over the River Beult. The man in charge of the repairs – the foreman – thought that there would be no train at that time of the day. So, his workmen took up the track.

The foreman got it wrong. His book of train times SAID there would be no train. He was looking at the wrong page of the book. In fact, it came nearly two hours earlier than he expected.

The express train was rushing down the track. The engine braked and skidded over the bridge with no rails and managed to reach the far side, but the wooden bridge cracked, and most of the carriages fell into the shallow river, the River Beult.

Mr Charles Dickens was on board with his young friend, Nell Ternan. He was a hero that day and helped many of the injured. He even held some of them as they died.

The shock of the crash has bothered him for the past five years. It made him ill and afraid of trains. The accident happened in 1865 on 9 June. Charles has died today, five years later ... on 9 June.

Charles raged against the Ragged Schools and the Industrial Schools. He has not lived long enough to see the new law that will be passed in August. It says that there will be schools for every child.

We do not have enough teachers yet, but the children can be put into classes of 80 pupils. One teacher can control all of those with the help of a strap, the cane, and other strong punishments, I am sure.

Charles was a ghost of a man after Staplehurst. Now he is a real ghost. Another of my friends gone to join my Albert.

1 May 1873

The great explorer, David Livingstone is dead. This wonderful Scotsman went to Africa and did not just teach the natives how to be Christian.

David Livingstone

He taught them how to live the British way. In return we will take their riches - gold and diamonds, sugar and tea and a lot more. We do NOT take slaves - even though it is one of Africa's richest trades. David did his best to stop that and we had to send our soldiers to the Gold Coast when the native leader, Kofi, tried to fight back. Foolish Kofi.

Natives must learn they cannot argue with our machine guns.

Most native chiefs are our trading partners now, so when we want to add those countries to my Empire it will be easier, won't it?

David has also taken my name around the world. He came upon one of the world's greatest waterfalls. The natives called them Mosi-oa-tunya – The Smoke that Thunders. Dear David gave them a new name. Victoria Falls. They will be known as that forever more in honour of me.

David had not been seen for a few years so newspaper reporter Henry Stanley set off to find dear David. Doctor Livingstone did not even know he was lost.

After walking hundreds of miles, through dozens of dangers, Stanley finally came across Livingstone and said those great words ...

Doctor Livingstone, I presume!

Now poor old David has died. His corpse was kneeling at his bedside, praying, when they found him.

Henry Stanley was hired by King Leopold of Belgium to help Belgium conquer the Congo area of Africa. (The bit in the middle).

Since bicycle tyres have been invented the world will pay a fortune for the rubber that grows on trees in the Congo. And the world was keen on ivory for billiard balls that grow on Elephants in the Congo – I mean the ivory grew on the elephants, not the billiard balls grew on the elephants. (Ha-ha).

King Leopold wants an empire like mine. But his Belgian explorers are much more vicious than people like my David.

A British trader reported ...

I watched a file of poor slave devils, chained by the neck. There were about a hundred of them trembling and fearful before the overseer, who strolled by whirling a whip. For each strong, healthy slave there were many like skeletons or dried up like mummies, their skin worn out, damaged by deep scars, covered with bleeding wounds. No matter how unfit they were, they all had to get on with the job. They were beasts of burden with bent legs.

British Trader

Any natives who rebelled against Leopold's rule had ears or noses sliced off. But worst was the way his army claimed their reward for capturing rebels - they chopped off an

African's hand and were paid for every hand they collected.

At lake Tumba, a Swedish missionary E. V. Sjoblom wrote,

> I saw dead bodies floating on the lake with the right hand cut off, and the officer told me when I came back why they had been killed. It was all part of the war for rubber. As I turned away one of the native policemen said, 'Oh, that is nothing, a few days ago I returned from a fight, and I brought the chief man 160 hands but he just threw them in the river'.

Still Henry Stanley did find David in those steaming jungles. I think that one day I shall make him 'Sir' Henry Stanley. David will be brought back and buried at Westminster Abbey with all the greatest of Great Brits.

23 January 1875

Poor Charles Kingsley has died at the age of 55. Of course, Charles wrote the book 'The Water Babies'. It was an attack on the dreadful treatment of little boys who were sent up chimneys to clean them.

It is a cheerful little story about 10-year-old Tom who suffers terribly as a chimney sweep. But do not worry, Tom falls into a river and drowns. Still that is all right because he is changed into a fishy water baby. The book made me cry when I read it.

Charles has died knowing there will be no more boys forced to suffer. A new law will stop it. Just two years ago Thomas Clark sent a chimney sweep lad up a 30cm wide pipe where the boy choked to death. Clark got six months in prison. That did not soot him. (Ha-ha).

A sweep told a newspaper reporter:

> The flesh of the boys must be hard. This is done by rubbing the elbows and knees with strong salt water. The child must stand close to a fierce fire as that is done. If the boy tries to move the sweep must beat him with a cane.

That had to stop. The world is getting kinder.

1 May 1876

A great day in British history. At last a law has been passed that makes me an Empress as well as a queen.

Prime Minister Disraeli passed the law today and about time too. I have been saying for years that I HAVE to be an empress. Nicholas in Russia calls himself Emperor and my son Alfred is married to his daughter. Nicholas calls her 'Empress'. I will NOT bow to my daughter-in-law.

My daughter, Vicky, is married to the son of William of Germany and HE calls himself Emperor. When William dies Vicky will be empress and I will not bow to my own daughter.

I have seen a map of the world and my Empire is coloured pink.

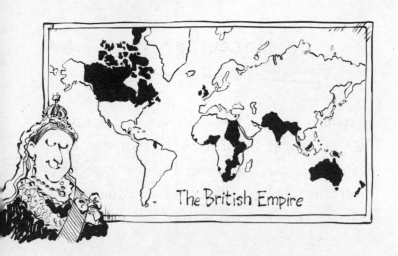

The British Empire

It spreads so wide it is always daytime somewhere in my empire. The sun never sets on my British Empire.

They say it is the
GREATEST EMPIRE IN THE WORLD
and now I AM ITS EMPRESS.
And about time.

28 December 1879

18 months ago, I took a railway trip across the Tay Bridge in Scotland. But now it has been struck by a storm and fallen into the River Tay. Sadly, a train was crossing and fell into the freezing waters below.

It was the worst storm Scotland had seen for 30 years with speeds of maybe 80 mph.

The signalman at St Fort Station watched the lights of the express train pass by then shrink into the night. A sudden gust clattered his cabin, he saw a flash of light from the bridge followed by Bible blackness. He tried to walk across the bridge but was blown back. He went down to the shore of the River Tay where it was more sheltered and at that moment the moon broke through the clouds. It showed a mangled and tangled wreckage of girders. There was no train.

75 people went to feed the fishes.

William McGonagall wrote one of his dramatic poems about the disaster.

Beautiful Railway Bridge of the Silv'ry Tay!
Alas! I am very sorry to say
That ninety lives have been taken away
On the last Sabbath day of 1879,
Which will be remember'd for a very long time.

McGonagall

127

Some people think his poetry is a joke. But he wrote a beautiful poem for his queen.

All hail to the Empress of India, Great Britain's Queen!
Long may she live in health, happy and serene;
Loved by her subjects at home and abroad;
Blest may she be when lying down
To sleep, and rising up, by the Eternal God

No matter what they say I think it is charming.

128

19 April 1881

And now my favourite Prime Minister has died. Benjamin Disraeli passed away today. I have had some odd Prime Ministers in my time, but I like Benjamin because he amused me. He wrote reports from parliament which were as amusing as his books.

Disraeli

There was a lot of argument about making me Empress, but my dearest Dizzy made sure it became law. I shall miss him.

The world is changing so much since Dizzy and I were born. Just two years ago Joseph Swan showed the world electric street lighting as bright as the sun. Our steamships roar across the Atlantic Ocean and bring back other wonders like Mr Edison's phonograph that will record voices. As well as the wonderful railways, we have telegraph wires that cross oceans and allow my people in Britain to speak to my people in the farthest corners of my empire.

Of course, it was our own Mr Fox Talbot who made cameras that anyone can work – that was back when I came to the throne. Now they are saying Mr Edison is working on moving pictures. I should like to see those.

We have the wonderful telephone from Mr Bell in America – maybe one day I will give Bell a ring. (Bell. Ring? Another of my little jokes). Now our inventors are working on making sound travel without telegraph wires. Something they call 'radio'.

In my age Britain has led the way with coal mines though it has had its tragedies. Just six months ago there was a sad disaster at Seaham mine in County Durham 164 men and boys died in a blast.

Some of the tales break my heart. One that touches me most was Michael Smith. Smith left his dying son at home while he went to work. After the explosion the men were trapped underground to die slowly. Smith had time to scratch a letter to his wife on his tin water-bottle with a rusty nail.

DEAR MARGARET
THERE WAS 40 OF US ALTOGETHER AT 7AM. SOME WAS SINGING HYMNS BUT MY THOUGHTS WAS ON MY LITTLE MICHAEL THAT HIM AND I WOULD MEET IN HEAVEN AT THE SAME TIME.
DEAR WIFE. FAREWELL. MY LAST THOUGHTS ARE ABOUT YOU AND THE CHILDREN. BE SURE AND TEACH THE CHILDREN TO PRAY FOR ME. OH WHAT AN AWFUL POSITION WE ARE IN. MICHAEL SMITH. 54 HENRY STREET.

And Smith had his sad wish. His son Michael did die on the same day as his father Michael. I hope they have met in heaven.

The explosion left 107 widows and 259 children without the men who made their money. I sent a telegram and £100 to tell them of my sorrow. Four boys were 14 years old; the oldest man was 71.

The widows were given twelve pence a week to live on. The miners went on strike for more but the owner of the mine, my Lord Londonderry, sacked them and threw them on the streets to starve. Their families were left with no food and no coal for cooking and heating in the harsh winter months. Five men were sent to jail.

Sad. But we rulers have to be strong and show the common people that we rule.

I hope the age of Victoria will be remembered for the lives we saved with clever people like

John Snow and Florence Nightingale. I hope
my age will be remembered for the things
that made life better – electric lights and
telephone.

Let us not spend too much time remembering
the lives we lost.

2 March 1882

I am shocked. I am shaken. But above all I am angry. A man tried to kill me. AGAIN.

I had stepped off the London train and was in my carriage on the way to Windsor Castle I heard some banging noises and thought it was some machine. The boys from Eton School had been there to cheer for me but now they were jumping on a man with a pistol and beating him.

Bang!

MaClean

Oh, how those people must love me. They risked their lives to save their queen.

The police tell me his name is Roderick Maclean and that he is quite mad. He will not be punished, just locked away in a mad house for the rest of his life.

Why? Why not execute the villain? He is assassin number seven and not ONE of them has been hanged. I asked for them to be executed. If they had executed the first one the others may not have tried.

But no. They say a dead assassin will become a hero to the rebels. Look at the other seven.

10 June, 1840 - Edward Oxford

I was leaving Buckingham Palace with dear Albert when a little mean-looking man fired two pistols. Edward Oxford - a bar-keeper - was just 18 years old. He said there were no bullets in his gun. The jury said he was mad, locked him away for 24 years then sent him off to Australia.

30 May, 1842 - John Francis

John Francis was the strangest and most dangerous case. Albert and I were riding home after a church service. Albert said an evil-looking rascal pointed a gun at us. He said the pistol sparked but didn't fire and the villain ran off.

Mr Peel, who invented the police force, said we had to catch him and we should ride out the next day and give the gunman another chance.

Mr Peel had detectives in the crowd and, sure enough, the young carpenter John Francis stepped forward and aimed his pistol. The detectives grabbed him. Imagine that? I was a real live target to catch an assassin.

The newspapers made it sound like a stage play ...

The court found him guilty and the judge said:

> It now only remains for me to pass upon you the sentence of the law, which is that you, John Frances, be taken from hence to the place from whence you came, that you be drawn from thence on a hurdle to the place of execution and that you be hanged by the neck until you be dead; that your head be afterwards severed from your body, and that your body be divided into four quarters, to be used in such manner as to her Majesty shall see fit. And the Lord have mercy on your soul.

Hanged, beheaded, and cut into quarters? That sounded good to me. But, again, they told me to spare his life. He was transported to Australia.

3 July, 1842 - John Bean

Just five weeks later John Bean, armed with a pistol, pushed his way to the front of a crowd waiting to see us pass. He was a hunch-backed newspaper seller, four foot tall. He filled his pistol with broken clay pipe and aimed at us as we rode out from Buckingham Palace. Two boys in the crowd caught him and handed him to the police. Little Bean said he wanted to be arrested so his miserable life could change. His pistol was filled with more tobacco than powder. He sent to jail for 18 months with hard labour.

19 June, 1849 - William Hamilton

Hamilton was standing on the exact spot where Edward Oxford stood nine years earlier. Can these pistol shooters not come up with a new idea?

He was an Irishman who had left his

homeland because of the hunger. He said he had powder but no bullet in his pistol and that if he were caught, he would go to prison and be fed. He was sent to prison in Gibraltar for 7 years where he could try and eat the apes that guard the rock. Silly man.

27 June, 1850 - Robert Pate

When I said I wanted the shooters to come up with a new idea I had no idea Robert Pate would attack me with a walking stick with an iron knob. He struck me on the head. My bonnet saved my skull from being crushed by the brute.

It left me with a black eye, and a scar that lasted for years. But two hours later I appeared before my people in Covent Garden to prove that I was well and that my injury would not stop me from doing my duty. Oh, how they loved me.

139

Pate had been in the army, which drove him mad, and he was sent to Tasmania for 7 years.

It is odd that the only assassin who did NOT use a gun was the only one who hurt me?

29 February, 1872 - Arthur O'Connor

The last attack before today was from a 17-year-old boy called O'Connor.

This young man climbed the fence at Buckingham Palace and raced across the courtyard without being seen. When my carriage returned to the palace entrance, O'Connor rushed up to its side and raised a flintlock pistol just inches away from me.

That was when the noble Scot, John Brown, clutched him by the neck and threw him to the ground. It seems O'Connor's pistol was broken and useless. O'Connor said he never

meant to hurt me, just frighten me. He wanted me to sign a paper that would set free Irish prisoners in British jails.

Of course, I gave dear John Brown a medal for his courage. O'Connor was sent prison for a year and given 20 strokes with a birch rod. Finally, he was sent to Australia.

I am over 60 now. Too frail to face such terrors. If only they had hanged the first ones.

29 March 1883

Sometimes I feel I have lived too long. So many friends have died and left me. Now my Scottish servant John Brown is dead. He was only 56. Six years younger than I.

He was as loyal a friend as my Albert. But John did not argue with me as much as Albert used to.

Every night I sleep with a plaster model of Albert's hand by my bed. When I go to my grave, I shall have BOTH men with me. I have left orders for a piece of John's hair to be cut off and buried with me.

I shall also have his photograph. It will be wrapped in white tissue paper and placed in my left hand, with flowers arranged to hide it from view. I want no scandal about me and John.

There are enough shocking stories going around about us. A servant noticed that he gave me his mother's wedding ring and wrote me letters when I was in London. I wear the ring on the third finger of my right hand as if we were married. We were not, but today I feel like a widow all over again.

I need John at this time. A dreadful newspaper called The Daily News is printing terrible things about my Empire. It says we are growing our Empire while we ignore the poor people back home in Britain. A reporter called George Sims is the worst. His grandfather was John Stevenson, one of those dreadful Chartists from many years ago.

George Sims

He is saying we must knock down the slums and put the poorest people in clean, new houses. And he thinks the rich should pay for this.

He is even pouring poison into the minds of people going to the theatre. Actors recite his cruel poem, 'It was Christmas Day in the Workhouse'. It tells of an old man whose wife was too proud to enter the workhouse. She begged him to find her a crust.

Then she rose to her feet and trembled, and fell on the rags and moaned,
And, 'Give me a crust, I'm famished... for the love of God,' she groaned.
'I rushed from the room like a madman and flew to the workhouse gate,
Crying, 'Food for a dying woman,' and the answer came, 'Too late.'
They drove me away with curses; then I fought with a dog in the street
And tore from the mongrel's clutches a crust he was trying to eat.'

The workhouse refused to help and, so she died.

The old man went back to rage against the workhouse governors.

George Sims also wrote a book with a chapter called 'Horrible London' and described the slum families and how the rent ruined them.

Let us take a few of the families. I will begin with the workers:

T. Harborne, stonemason, occupies two ramshackle rooms, which are in a filthy condition. Has five children. Total weekly income through slackness, 8 shillings. Rent, 4½ shillings.

E. Williams, trader, two rooms in a court which is a hotbed of disease. Has eight children. Total earnings, 17 shillings. Rent, 5½ shillings.

T. Briggs, labourer, one room, four children. Rent, 4 shillings. No furniture; all sleep on floor. Daughter answered knock, absolutely naked; ran in and covered herself with a sack.

Mrs. Johnson, widow, one room, three children. Earnings, 6 shillings. Rent, 3½ shillings.

W. Leigh, fancy box-maker, two awful rooms, four children. Earnings, 14 shillings. Rent, 6 shillings.

H. Walker, hawker, two rooms, seven children. Earnings, 10 shillings. Rent, 5½ shillings.

E. Thompson, out of work, five children. Living by pawning goods and clothes. Wife drinks. Rent, 4 shillings.

G. Garrard, labourer, out looking for work, eight children. No income. Rent, 5½ shillings. Pawning last rags. Starving. Refuses to go into workhouse.

But the Bible says, 'The Poor will always be with us.' Always. I cannot do anything about it. One woman cannot change the cruel world. Unless that woman is Florence Nightingale, of course.

I wish I had John to tell me I am right.

16 November 1888

Last year was a time when the British people were joyous. It was fifty years since I came to the throne and we had a great service at Westminster Abbey. 300 voices sang one of Albert's songs for me. People lined the streets and cheered.

Across the land a thousand bonfires blazed and a million fireworks fizzed.

There were parties around the Empire from Canada to Singapore where prisoners were set free and sick patients in hospital were given extra rice.

That was 21 June last year.

But this year in London the mood is one of fear and terror. Five women have been murdered and cut apart by a man who calls himself 'Jack the Ripper.' Fear walks the streets and my police are helpless. The man must be caught. The pictures in the newspapers are horrific.

And this year there is more unrest in the streets. The girls who make and sell matches have been on strike for better pay. Today they won their fight for safer work, better food, and more pay. My minister explained in a report.

MATCH MAKERS

Making matches means dipping the wooden sticks into phosphorus ... the explosive bit on the end. The white phosphorus is poisonous and after a while it gives the matchmakers 'phossy jaw' – the fumes eat at their jawbones, leaving them with empty cheeks that ooze foul-smelling liquid, cause brain damage and then death from organ failure. The disease can rip off a girl's jaw – they are usually girls - and lead to a slow, painful death.

A group of girls working in a London factory went on strike and won. The factory owners will replace white phosphorus with the safer red phosphorus.

But there are still young home-workers, using white phosphorus to their cost. Several younger children in their families died from eating these matches.

Lord Londonderry crushed the miners when they went on strike and showed the workers must obey their bosses. If poor little girls can win this sort of fight it may give working class workers ideas that they have the power to argue with their owners.

There is even talk that their battle has showed the way for women who want to vote. They call themselves suffragettes. Votes for women will never happen.

Of course, I said electric underground trains would never happen. Now I hear they will open in London inside two years.

THE WORLD IS CHANGING SO FAST I CANNOT KEEP UP.

1 July 1890

From today my Empire takes over Uganda
and Zanzibar in Africa. We have agreed with
Germany to swap them for our island of
Heligoland in the North Sea.

I am not pleased. Germany is a ruthless
and cruel empire. My poor
people of Heligoland have
been handed over. Still,
there are more pink
patches of the
British Empire on
the map.

10 June 1896

In my long life I have had ten children. They are grown up and happy. Many are married into the great royal families of Europe. But the poor are not so lucky. When they cannot afford to bring up a baby, they hand it over to a Baby Farmer. Today the Baby Farmer Amelia Dyer was hanged.

Amelia Dyer

Poor parents had been giving this wicked woman five or ten pounds and she would care for the baby till she found it a new home ... she said. Amelia Dyer just took the money and killed the children.

In March last year a bargeman pulled the corpse of a baby out of the Thames. It was wrapped in a parcel – but the paper had been used to send a parcel to Mrs. Dyer, so her name and address was on it. By the time Mrs Dyer was arrested six more of the little corpses had been found.

No one will ever know how many she murdered, but at the time of her arrest she had been baby-farming for fifteen years.

Like many wicked women she had a song
written about her execution and the way she
would roast in Hell...

Sing along ...

> ## The Old Baby Farmer
> The old baby farmer has been executed
> It's about time she was put out of the way
> She was a bad woman it is not disputed
> Not a word in her favour can anyone say
>
> Down through the trapdoor she's quickly
> disappearing
> Her poor little victims in front of her eyes
> The sound of her own death bell she'll be
> a-hearing
> The rope round her neck ... how quickly
> time flies

Dear Mr Dickens could have made a story
about her. But he is long gone. So many of
the people I have known are dead. Dead as
Albert, my Albert.

20 November 1896

A new amusement has arrived from America. The moving picture shows. They tell me the 'movies' show dancing, boxing and waves breaking on a beach. The inventors are working with sound records so viewers can see dramas with sound as well as pictures.

Just as clever are cameras that can look INSIDE the body with something they call x-rays. I do NOT want any doctor looking inside me, thank you very much.

And a new law says motor cars can travel at 14 miles an hour. Until now they have had to stay below 4 miles an hour and have a man with a red flag walking in front of them.

One day someone will die in a speeding car. You will see.

22 June 1897

Sixty years on the throne. More than anyone in history. I drove through London as crowds cheered. I even drove through poor areas like Southwark. How the people love their Empress.

Long live the Queen!

Viva Victoria!

24 May 1899

MY 80TH BIRTHDAY.

My Grandson Kaiser Wilhelm II of Germany
came to see me. He is a strange young man.

Nobody likes poor Willy. I can see why. I
cannot stand him. My daughter, (his mother),
once refused to wish him a happy birthday ...
so he sulked for days. His father thought he
would be a dangerous leader. But Willy is
now King of Germany and we shall see.

I think he is cruel because he is unhappy with
the way he looks. He was born with a
withered left arm and it embarrasses him.
When he is photographed, he insists that he

hides his weak arm. People around him are made to hide their strong left arms too.

His German workers went on strike just like so many of my British workers. We talk to them and sometimes bully them. With the match-girls we even gave in to them. But not Willy.

He ordered soldiers to attack the strikers.

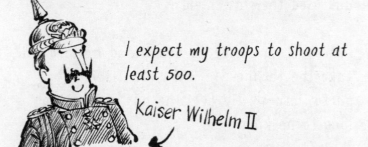

I expect my troops to shoot at least 500.

Kaiser Wilhelm II

He wants a German empire as great as mine. Sooner or later his empire and Britain's will clash. He sees Britain and France as his enemies. That will mean war.

There have been too many wars in my lifetime. There is a war in South Africa now against the Dutch settlers - the Boers. The Boers are just simple farmers. Yet they are winning. How can that be? My ministers are saying it is the start of the end of the British Empire. I do not want to live to see that.

My brave soldiers have already defeated the fierce natives - the Zulus. The Zulus fell in heaps as they ran at our machine guns. They simply stopped to pick up their dead friends and used them as shields.

I am getting closer to death and Edward will take the throne. He will have a secret party, I think. He feels he has waited too long to be king.

NOT LONG NOW, EDWARD.
NOT LONG.

31 December 1900

THE END OF A HORRIBLE YEAR.

The Boer war is going badly. In April, my eldest son Edward was shot at as he travelled through Belgium. The gun was fired by a young boy who wanted an end to the Boer War. Edward lived but we all live in fear now.

Bored war

My daughter, Vicky, is dying in great pain from cancer. In August I was told my favourite son Alfred had died from throat cancer. My poor darling Affie.

A few weeks later I heard that my lovely grandson Prince Victor had died of a fever in the Boer War. My God but I do hate that war.

Then Jane, Lady Churchill, my oldest and most trusted friend, was found dead in her bed here at Osborne Palace. It was on Christmas Day. I remember how my Albert made Christmas a great event in Britain. Mr Charles Dickens and his 'Christmas Carol' book made it a time of happiness and giving.

Albert. Charles. Alfred. Now Jane. All gone.

I once feasted in my palaces but now I have lost my love of food. I am growing thinner and so weak I need a wheelchair. If dear John Brown were here, he would push me along the way he helped me with my pony. John is gone.

I am almost blind and forget things. I asked my Doctor Sir James Reid if I was getting better.

Am I better? I should like to live a little longer, as I have still a few things to settle

Yes, Your Majesty has been very ill, but you are now better.

22 January 1901

I am surrounded by my children and Grandchildren. The family have crowded into my small bedroom where the Bishop of Winchester is reciting prayers and hymns.

I found the strength to talk to my doctor.

Sir James, I'm very ill.

Your Majesty will soon be better.

I think he is lying to me.

Edward is waiting for my last breath so he can become king. Even the strange young Kaiser Wilhelm of Germany is here. Willy has

been sitting at my left side for more than two hours, propping me up with his one good arm.

The room is starting to fill with the sound of sobbing and weeping and the chanting of the bishop.

Each son, daughter and grandchild is taking a turn to kiss my hand and say farewell.

Yes, this is farewell. Farewell to my empire but hello again to my Albert, my John, my Charles, my Dizzy, Jane and Affie and King Uncle William.

My final journey. What was it that William Shakespeare said?

JOURNEYS END IN LOVERS MEETING.

Shakespeare

Epilogue

Victoria died on 22 January 1901.

Doctor Reid prepared the queen for her coffin, with the help of Mrs Tuck, the queen's dresser. The queen had refused to be preserved like a mummy. It would take a month to arrange a funeral in London so her body would start to rot. They scattered charcoal on the floor of the coffin to soak up the rot and stop the smell.

Mrs Tuck cut off Victoria's hair, dressed her in a white silk dressing gown and placed her wedding veil over her face. They called her sons, the Kaiser Wilhelm, and the new king Edward to lift her body into the coffin.

The family then left, while Doctor Reid and Mrs Tuck carried out the queen's secret orders.

John Brown's mother's wedding ring was placed on her finger; a photo of Brown and a piece of his hair were laid beside her, along with Brown's handkerchief. These were all carefully hidden from view. From husband Albert there was a dressing gown along with a plaster cast of his hand.

The queen was now ready for her final journey. A train took her coffin to London. Which station? Victoria station, of course.

Lots of mistakes were made and Kaiser Willy blamed the Bishop of Winchester. He said...

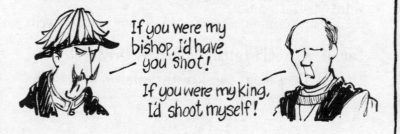

If you were my bishop, I'd have you shot!

If you were my king, I'd shoot myself!

The coffin was taken on another train to Windsor station where a carriage was waiting to take it to Windsor Castle. But the horses broke free and snapped their reins. The coffin was pulled by 130 sailors instead.

It arrived an hour too early and everyone had to hang around for an hour in the cold.

The funeral had cost £35,500, which would be £2.8 million today.

Victoria had filled 141 books with her diary. When she died her daughter, Beatrice, read them and cut out all the dreadful parts that would upset the family. They were then burned so we only have what Beatrice wanted us to see.

But if we could rescue Victoria's Dreadful Diaries they may look like the ones in this book.

END

INDEX

Aborigines 81–2, 112

Afghanistan 47–51

Africa 46, 117–21, 151, 159

Albert of Saxe-Coburg (prince) 18–19

  alive 34–5, 41, 44–5, 66–8, 74–5, 136, 142, 162

  dead 95–9, 103, 109, 116, 147, 154, 165, 167

America 29–30, 65, 108, 155

assassins 134–41

Atlantic Ocean 29, 32, 130

Australia 44–6, 80–1, 112, 135, 137, 141

Balmoral Castle 54, 68–9

Barrett, Michael (activist) 107–9

Belgium 119–20, 161

Bell, Alexander (inventor) 130

Boer War 160–2

bridges 69, 91, 114–15, 126–7

British Empire 26, 32, 46, 82, 94, 118, 120, 124–5, 130, 143, 147, 151, 159–60, 165

Brown, John (Victoria's servant) 68, 140–3, 145–6, 162, 165–7

Brunel, Isambard (engineer) 32, 55

Brunel, Marc (engineer) 55–6

Brydon, William (doctor) 51–2

Buckingham Palace 13, 24–5, 39, 61, 69, 86, 135, 138, 140

Calcraft, William (hangman) 109–10

cameras 130, 155

Canada 46, 65, 147

Cayley, George (inventor) 56

Chartists (activists) 45, 60–2, 143

children 29–31, 52–4, 59, 63, 77–81, 89–92, 97–8, 101, 116, 122–3, 131–2, 145–6, 152–4, 164–5

chimney sweeps 80, 122–3

cholera (disease) 83–6, 102

Christmas 96–9, 110, 144, 162

Conroy, John (royal adviser) 16, 20

convicts 80–1, 112

coronation 21–3

cotton 30–1, 76, 93

Crimean War 87

criminals 80–1, 90, 108

Crystal Palace 72–4, 78

Dash (dog) 13, 16

diamonds 75–6, 83, 86, 117

Dickens, Charles (author) 33-4, 37, 90-1, 110-11, 114-16, 154, 162
diseases 58, 67, 79, 82-5, 88, 95-6, 145, 149
Disraeli, Benjamin (prime minister) 58-9, 124, 129, 165
doctors 43, 84-6, 88, 95, 97, 113, 118, 155, 163-4, 166
Dyer, Amanda (baby farmer) 152-3

East India Company 93-4
Edison, Thomas (inventor) 130
Edward VII (British king) 160-1, 164, 166
electricity 101, 129-30, 133, 150
Elphinstone, William (general) 48-50
Equiano, Olaudah (writer) 27-8

factories 76-8, 149
famines 57-8, 63, 67, 93, 99
Frankenstein (novel) 63
funerals 15, 20, 64, 98-9, 166, 168

George IV (British king) 11-13, 15, 42, 44
Germany 16, 42-3, 96-8, 124, 151, 158-9, 164
Gibraltar 14, 139
Great Exhibition 72-5
Great Game 47-8, 52

Hardy, Thomas (author) 103
Hyde Park Fair 104-6

India 46-7, 49, 75-6, 83, 92-3, 128
Ireland 57, 59, 63, 65-7, 95, 99, 107-8, 111, 138-9, 141

Jack the Ripper (serial killer) 147-8

Kingsley, Charles (author) 122

laws, lots of 26-7, 34, 38, 52-3, 81, 89-90, 102, 111, 116, 122, 124, 129, 137, 156
Leopold (Belgian king) 119-20
Light Brigade (horse soldiers) 87
Livingstone, David (explorer) 117-21

McGonagall, William (poet) 127-8
machine guns 118, 160
matches 91, 148-9, 159
mills 30, 77-8
mines 52, 130-1, 149
moving pictures (films) 130, 155

newspapers 14, 45, 83, 102-3, 110, 118, 123, 136, 138, 143, 148
Nightingale, Florence (nurse) 88, 133, 146

Oliver Twist (novel) 33-4, 37

Parliament 43, 57-8, 60, 129
Pearson, Charles (inventor) 100
peasants 57, 63, 65
Peel, Robert (policeman) 136

poetry 12-13, 40, 75, 103, 127-8, 144
police 101, 107, 121, 135-6, 138, 148
poor people 34-7, 83-4, 86, 89, 144-6, 152
postage stamps 38-9
potatoes 35, 37, 57-8
prisons/prisoners 93, 107-9, 111, 122, 139, 141, 147
punishments 27, 77-8, 81, 116, 135

railways 53, 55-6, 69-71, 74, 100-3, 114-15, 127, 150, 167
Reid, James (doctor) 163-4, 166
rivers 55, 61, 69, 126, 153
Russia 47, 87, 101, 124

schools 53, 89-91, 116, 134
Scotland 26, 53, 56, 68, 99, 126, 142
sewers, stinking 54, 84, 86
Shelley, Mary (author) 63
Sheridan, Richard (playwright) 18
ships 13-14, 28, 32, 65, 81, 83, 130
silk 30-1, 93, 166
Sims, George (reporter) 143-5
slavery 26-31, 82
slums 35, 54, 101, 144-6
Smith, Michael (miner) 131-2
Snow, John (doctor) 84-6, 133
songs 13, 21-2, 31, 109-10, 147, 154
Stanley, Henry (reporter) 118-19, 121
starvation 36, 58, 63, 67, 93, 95, 101, 132, 139, 144, 146

steam power 32, 75, 100, 130
Stephenson, George (engineer) 70
Stephenson, Robert (engineer) 69-70
strikes 132, 148-9, 159
suffragettes (activists) 150
Swan, Joseph (inventor) 129-30

Talbot, Fox (inventor) 130
Tasmania 81-2, 112-13, 140
telephones 130, 133
Thackeray, William (poet) 75
typhoid (disease) 95-6

underground railways 55-6, 100-3, 150

Westminster Abbey 21, 121, 147
Wilberforce, William (activist) 27
Wilhelm II (German kaiser) 158-9, 164-7
William IV (British king) 11, 13-16, 19-20, 34, 44, 112, 165
Windsor Castle 13, 15, 95, 98-9, 103, 134, 168
women 51, 59, 62-3, 88, 92, 98-9, 101, 145-6, 150, 152-3
workhouses 34-7, 144-6
working class 30, 76, 78, 132, 145, 149, 159

Zulus 160

LOOK OUT FOR

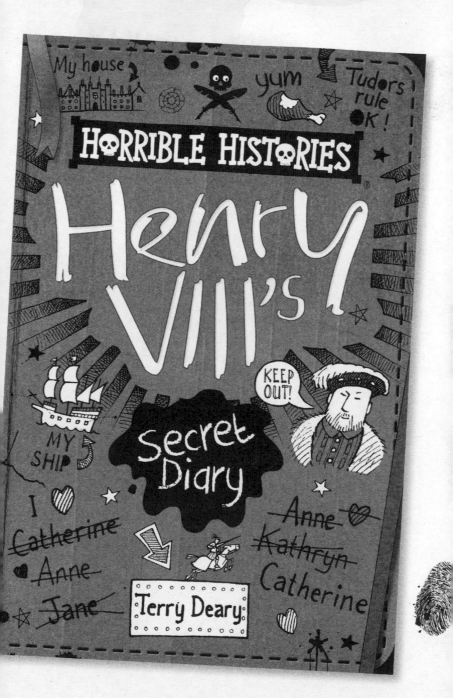